Preface

Like any brother and sister, Jerry and Lillian share common interests while playing together and learn to get along when conflicts occur. Yet they are also a special pair of siblings: Due to a rare genetic mutation, they were both diagnosed with leukemia at a very young age (Jerry at three and Lillian at six). The cancer is aggressive and relentless, but they fought hard, never giving up hope. Between the two of them, there have been three bone marrow transplants, months of hospitalization, and countless sufferings.

Jerry and Lillian have quite different personalities: Jerry is intelligent, observing, and a little reserved. Lillian, on the other hand, is cheerful, spontaneous, and carefree. As a parent, it is heartbreaking to watch each of them fight cancer in their own resilient way. At the same time, I feel extremely proud of them and of our family as a whole. To have a child diagnosed with cancer is a terrifying experience, to have two children with the same disease is simply beyond bearing. I don't know how we have come this far, but I am certain we are still standing together as a family because of faith, hope and love, as is manifested in this collection of poems, drawings, and stories created by Jerry and Lillian. I hope their works can bring hope and strength to families struck with childhood cancer.

Mother of Jerry & Lillian

1

Contents

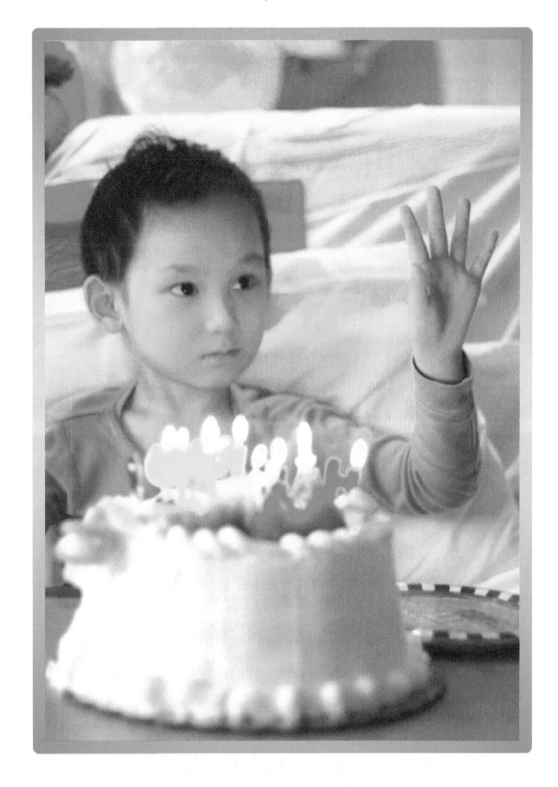

Fight, Love, and Hope

Jerry was diagnosed with leukemia at the tender age of three. He endured two bone marrow transplants with numerous complications: visual impairment, renal failure, cardiomyopathy, to name just a few. Through all these sufferings and hardship, Jerry stays strong and hopeful. Just like he said in his poem: "Life is a war, and I am the warrior." Jerry truly is a WARRIOR.

The War of Life

Life is a challenge-filled war of hardship and pain.

In every new season I face a new battle.

Through shine and through rain,

I must fight till my bones rattle!

Stronger still, my enemies grow,

Yet, failure is not an option!

Whether it be swift or slow,

I will strive forward powered by determination!

Though the battle rages on,

The bloodshed does not subside,

And I haven't yet won,

I shall not run nor hide.

For only the warrior is the victor,

And only the perseverant will laugh to the end.

No matter the pain or the torture,

I will fix and mend

My broken heart and soul,

Whenever my enemies attempt to crush me.

I will achieve my final goal,

And truly become who I wanna be!

In the dark world of childhood cancer, where the fight for life takes precedence over everything else, the pursuit of happiness may be naïve. But can you deny a child's wish to be happy, his desire to achieve what he wants, and his efforts to keep going with hope?

Joy

A pure sense of Joy,

Of which language cannot describe,

And nothing can destroy.

A sunshiny, upbeat vibe,

That keeps me in step,

As I strive forward and far,

With no way to sidestep.

Reaching for the brightest star,

Moving forward like a soldier,

Strong and steady,

Wanting to be happier,

And become who I want to be.

I withheld my sadness

When things get hard,

Keeping my eyes on the light in the darkness,

As I keep guard,

Fighting for happiness.

I am grateful for this joy that gave me hope,

And I will not give up or quit,

Even as my hand slips off the rope,

And I start falling again bit by bit.

No matter how many failed attempts and tries,

I will keep fighting for my glorious destiny,

Until I see it with my very own eyes,

And truly become who I wanna be!

Jerry has never physically attended a school since Kindergarten for medical reasons, but he is aware of the bullies that may occur among kids. He wrote this poem to voice his attitude against bullies: "What's meant to bring you down, shall only build you up through the roof."

Unstoppable

Call me weird, call me strange.

Call me different from the normal range.

Call me all the things that you are.

But your regret shall come in a time not too far.

One day you will realize how wrong these words are to speak.

Call me timid, call me weak,

But not for long,

Cause I'm strong.

Look at me of the present,

Look at me from the current.

Like a chrysanthemum, I am joyful,

Like a rose, in pain yet hopeful.

Yet who would have known the silent tears

That I've shed in the dark,

Who would have guessed the pain of the years

That left such a deep mark.

They'd laughed at me,

And they'd scoffed at who I want to be.

They teased and taunted,

They harassed and haunted.

Yet I did not give up fighting back,

And I did not crumple to the floor.

Brave I stood 'gainst their attack,

And I opened the door.

To y'all who struggle in pain,

Feeling no hospitality,

Feeling forever rain,

And feeling unloved and hated by all you see,

Let me give you this knowledge of truth:

What's meant to bring you down

Shall only build you up through the roof

Of mean words and let fade your frown.

Your enemies shall mesmerize,

As you rise.

Mean words and torture

Shall not stop your fantastic future

"If winter comes, can spring be far behind?" In his most painful days and darkest moments, Jerry longs for Spring, because Spring represents promise, hope, and the regeneration of life.

Spring Time

Spring time spring time,

It's here at last.

A little tune and a beautiful rhyme,

We shall celebrate and forget all the pain from the past.

The weather is shining and beautiful,

The flowers blossom and grow.

Wherever you may go,

Remember to stay joyful,

For spring is refreshment.

It's time to make the big discovery!

Experience the enjoyment,

And rejoice and be happy!

Relish the glamorous spring morning,

Love the wonderful terrain of spring.

Spring is the solution of how to restart,

When the pain of the world is hanging over your heart.

So live it well,

Live it with hope,

Live it with joy.

Have joyful stories with joyful plots to tell,

For spring is here to bring a new beginning.

Raise your head and sing!

Embark on your journey of dreams,

And follow the sunshine beams!!!

Jerry wrote this poem to express his desire for freedom to pursue his dream.

If I Could Fly

If I could fly,

I would soar high and high

Into the vast blue sky,

And gaze down upon the world with my eye.

If I had wings,

I would ride the wind and the breeze;

I would let the sadness melt as I am the one who sings;

I would glide above the seas and the trees

Through the misty sunlit air,

To a remote quiet place,

Where all is peace and fair.

There I shall live with joy and grace,

Forever happy,

Forever free.

Yet such a beloved location,

Of which I'm drawn to,

Will be always nothing more than a dream in my imagination.

It's a dream I tell you

Never to be real,

Never reality.

Yet I still feel

That feathers and wind ain't the only solution to being happy.

I will fly,

Not by wings of any kind,

But by love and friendship.

Strong will stay my heart and mind,

Through pain and hardship,

Till my dreams come true,

And with love I flew!

Life Is Just a Book

Life is like a book.

The days turned to pages.

Turn around and have a look

At what may seem like ages.

Sometimes things happen from good to bad,

Like a main character's life being woven,

Joyful and sad,

Yet so impossible and disbelieving,

As if fiction or not real.

Yet you live through it knowing

And understanding the feel

Of pain and the joy of a main character.

Yet still confused of why the playwright seems to revolve around you,

And why the gist seems to be including no one otherwise.

And what should you do?

So just stand up and rise.

Step out of your little threshold of fake safety,

Face life and win the war,

Because can't you see?

You can open the door,

Because you are the main character of the book and your life.

Stand up and fight,

Shatter pain's knife,

Exhilarate your blood,

Shred the weight of suffering and take flight.

You can win the battle.

Failure is not in your blood.

Let your bones rattle,

As you walk from your pain-hood,

And face your enemy head on.

Destroy and crush sadness and pain.

You have won.

You shall reign.

Victory is collectible but only when you strive for more.

It's very obtainable.

You just need to know who it's for,

Because it's yours and no one other.

It's yours to obtain,

And yours to keep,

Because you are the main character.

Wings of Fire

Jerry is a fan of the book series: Wings of Fire. He's listened to every book of the series (Because of visual impairment, Jerry reads primarily through audiobooks.) He wrote a poem to describe each tribe of the dragons in Wings of Fire.

SANDWING

Shiny, splendid, sandy scales,

Scorpion barbed deadly tails,

Majestic colors of sunlit sand,

Rulers of the desert land.

Wings of Fire, Poems by Jerry

LEAFWING

Green as trees with leaf-like wings,

Near extinction after the tree wars,

Split in two: Poisonwings and Sapwings,

Leaf-speak, vengeance,

and peace became tribe-splitting sores.

Wings of Fire, Poems by Jerry

SKYWING

Strong and steady,

Soaring swiftly,

Red and orange sunset scales,

Their flames wrote a scorching tale.

Wings of Fire, Poems by Jerry

ICEWING

Blue and white, like frosty snow,

Their scales are polished ice.

Frost breath freezes their ferocious foe,

Talon sharp as they slice.

Wings of Fire, Poems by Jerry

SEAWING

Ocean blue and sea green,

Luminescent scales blink a language.

The best swimmers to be seen,

Water breathing is their greatest advantage.

Wings of Fire, Poems by Jerry

MUDWING

Hidden beneath swamp and soil,

Holding their breath and blending in,

At warm temperatures, a fire can boil.

Families called troops are led by kin.

Wings of Fire, Poems by Jerry

HIVEWING

Four wings at birth, with bee-striped scales,

Multi-range powers and one hive-mind,

Nine hives ruled by royal females,

Finally freed from the Othermind's bind.

Wings of Fire, Poems by Jerry

RAINWING

Changing colors according to emotions,

Venomous spits that work on organisms,

Complex past, united present,

and a future of expectations,

Their queen now rules with courage and symbolism.

Wings of Fire, Poems by Jerry

NIGHTWING

Dark as night, speckled with stars,

Obtaining powers from the moon so far,

Reading minds and predicting the future,

Their tribe triumphed over pain and torture.

Wings of Fire, Poems by Jerry

SILKWING

Butterfly beauty, a collage of colors,

Sprouting four wings at the age of six,

Silver silk, flame silk, innate spinners,

Secret resistance called Chrysalis hidden in the mix.

Wings of Fire, Poems by Jerry

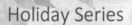

On Thanksgiving, Jerry wrote a poem to thank all who have supported him in his journey as a YouTuber.

Thank Y'all

Thank y'all for being a part,

Of my life as a YouTuber.

Thank y'all from deep within my heart.

Whether you are a viewer or subscriber,

And to those of you who are watching right now,

I will say "Happy Thanksgiving!"

I don't know since when, or even how,

But here we are thanking and rejoicing!

Christmas and New Year: Jerry wrote quite a few poems around the biggest holiday season to express his anticipation and determination about the year to come.

The Importance of Christmas

The importance of Christmas day

Is to rejoice and celebrate,

To show kindness in whatever we say,

To patiently await,

What we know is true.

And leave the pain behind,

Even though we may not have a clue,

Or any plan in mind.

Yet, there's something you need to know,

That peace and hope are existent always,

That upon Christmas's arrival,

It'll be the end of your painful days!

Christmas

Christmas shall soon be here.

It is time to celebrate!

May joy be everywhere,

And hope follow you,

Wherever you may be.

Let love be constant in whatever you may do,

For it is time to be happy!

A Christmas Tree in Washington

Christmas tree in Washington,

There you are, now I see.

Searching the states one by one,

At last I find my Christmas tree.

The best of the best,

The greenest of the green,

Better than all the rest,

The best I have ever seen.

So green and bright,

A shade that is yet to be named,

With dazzling beauty and flickering light,

This tree shall be claimed

By me alone.

For this Christmas tree suits me well,

It is mine to own.

And as you can tell

From the words above

That this amazing tree

I truly love,

So give it to me.

I will decorate it great.

It will be a beauty to the eye.

Just you wait,

For this is the best Christmas tree

One could ever buy.

New Year

With the arrival of a brand new year,

Come joy and hope and another step closer to my life-long goal.

There shall be no pain or fear,

Nothing but the flames of determination shall burn within my soul.

Though life may drag on through hardship and pain,

My heart within will not falter nor despair.

No matter the conditions, shine or rain,

Whether it be rewarding or unfair,

My eyes are set and looking straight,

My gaze falls upon only my destination,

I stride forward unaffected by the pain and the heavy weight.

I walk the path of my own decision,

For I know, one does not walk further than others by following their way,

And that the path to success is the path unknown.

It's the path I take, living day by day,

It's the path I create, and it's for me alone.

I will not hide nor cry,

For It's a new year to come.

I shall soar to the sky,

And ride the wind to my dream and who I wanna become!

My Regrets

My regrets from last year to now

Is that I didn't work so hard on my YouTube channel.

It's about what I let happen and what I allow.

Like a compressed volcano,

I'd held it all in

When I should have let go,

And let anger and pain flow away.

But now I know,

From the new year resolution I write today.

Not again will I make the same mistakes.

Whatever I may face,

Whatever it takes,

I will make right what I have done wrong,

And I will finish the race.

I could have kept a friend,

If I had done something right.

But I didn't know so till I reached the end.

Through the day and night,

Through the weeks and months,

I thought and wandered.

But now I know I have won,

Not because I have made a correct choice,

Of which I have pondered,

But because I have learned a lesson and found new knowledge.

So, goodbye to the frowning me.

I'm smiling now in my heart and eyes.

I know who I want to be.

I want to be the dove that flies,

Soaring through the whisper of the night

Upon the wind and through and the long,

Practically squealing with happiness,

Singing a song,

And being joyful and worriless.

That's who I am.

Hello, Past Me

Oh, hello me of the past,

I have too much to say to thee.

Do not feel estranged or outcast.

Life's not easy,

But there is no need to be distraught,

Or worry about other criteria.

Do not let thyself be caught

Within your enemies' deadly claws of bacteria.

They are poisonous filled talents.

But your faith is greater than the those who try to stop you.

Your path upon the web of life is woven,

And by you alone no one shall tell you what to do.

Treasure the good things you gain,

For all great things don't last.

And if its sunshine today that you obtain,

Tomorrow may be a rainy day.

You must learn to be proficient,

To aim for what you seek,

And be truly magnificent.

Fight on week after week,

And you will climb to the highest peak!

Dear future me,

Are you upset or happy?

Wherever you may be,

Let yourself see the true and amazing beauty.

For in life, hope is key!

Let me inspire with these very words

People across the planet worldwide.

To fly like morning birds,

Even if pain does not subside.

But most importantly,

I want to inspire myself,

To invoke future me,

To learn to be happy,

And to walk away from wistful memories.

For when you look around,

You will find evidence and see

That you have power no one has ever found!

Do not interrogate yourself on what you've done wrong.

We've all made mistakes.

The important thing is to move along,

Determined to succeed whatever it takes!

Life is a book.

You are the main character!

A little narrative poem about valentine party with friends

Valentine

It's valentine.

The sky is vast and clear.

The sun shall shine,

And the weather is just fine.

He twitched one ear.

Was that his friends calling his name?

He raced there to check it out.

His friends were all there looking the same.

With joyful smiles they all shouted,

"Happy Valentine!"

He distinguished the party host with ease,

His eyes shining with excitement.

"Look at these."

His other friend made an announcement.

It was some good bagels and sandwiches
with cheese in it.

They all ate bagel,

Gradual and slow.

They ate their food bit by bit.

Then they gave each other a card

That said, "Happy Valentine!"

"Life is not always hard," Jack said laughing,

Ready for some celery sandwiches,

Special creations of mine.

The host asked the hungry gang.

Everyone got an admittance slip

To a special Valentine's food shed.

They had sandwiches to eat and juice to sip.

Jack raised his head,

And shouted with pleasure.

The group cheered loud,

"Joy is a great treasure!!"

The host announced and bowed.

That's a happy Valentine's Day

But that's also all I have to say.

Fireworks

It's a peaceful July fourth night.

I lie calm and thoughtful,

Imagining the splash of light

'Cross the sky, so elegant and beautiful.

I hear the fireworks boom.

Their crackle in the distance.

Peace fills the room.

And gone are all the disturbance.

I think maybe this is freedom;

Maybe this is true peace;

Maybe I can relax;

Maybe the pain will cease.

Jerry is not alone in his fight against cancer. He is always surrounded with love from his family, church fellowship, and even people he doesn't know. Jerry loves his family. These are some poems he wrote about his family and friends.

Mother's Day of 2021

My Good Mother

My good mother,

Like a glowing shimmering star,

Of which one can see from afar.

Casting its brightest light,

Standing out amongst all in the night.

Purely and most certainly beautiful,

Indeed, truly amazing and wonderful,

My good mother.

Mother's Day of 2022

Mom You Are…

Mom, you are the soaring white dove.

Your beauty, true and undeniable,

Your flowing warmth and love

Cocoons me, body, mind, and soul.

Oh! Mom, you are the brightest star.

You cast your beautiful light near and far,

Illuminating my path as I move along.

And like the most beautiful song,

Your voice flows around me.

Like a lovely melody,

It calms my heart.

A wonderful piece of art

Cannot compare to you.

What the best music can do,

The tune of your voice exceeds.

My Dad, My King

My dad, my king,

You stay with me as I'm fighting.

Your protection stands like a mountain,

Your love surrounds me like a fountain.

A dream within dreams,

A fantastic treasure that gleams.

You fight with me side by side

When there is nowhere to hide.

You are sturdy and strong

At all times from now to infinite long.

I could not ask for a better father,

My king, my friend, and my protector!

You shall be by my side forever and ever!

Jerry's grandparents are in China, but that doesn't prevent them from showing their love and care. Jerry video chats with his grandparents almost every night.

My Time with Grandparents

Relaxed on my chair with my iPad,

My fingers dancing across the screen,

My facetime with grandparents truly makes me glad.

Writing with grandpa the best stories ever to be seen:

Stories about struggling in the blizzard,

Tiny bird and human escaping through the underbrush,

Horrible nights and an evil wizard.

It's a true legend as characters strive and rush

To complete the prophecy and save the Ocean of Peace.

And the city that is called Ever- life!

The adventures never cease,

Even when the bird finds a deadly knife against its throne and ready to kill,

His friend will not fail to protect him until,

Success is obtained and they have reached the end of the trail.

When my grandma joins to see me,

I would tell her through the screen,

"You are amazing and you make me happy!"

For she is the best grandma anyone can ever see!

She is kind and loving and likes to eat,

Veggies and fruits and delicious meat.

My grandparents are truly wonderful.

My grandpa is kind, my grandma is beautiful.

No grandparents are better than them!

Joshua is a boy of the same age as Jerry. Both of them like Minecraft. They used to play Minecraft over zoom every now and then, but Joshua's school life got busy so he was not able to play with Jerry anymore. Jerry wrote a poem to thank him.

Thank you, Joshua

Oh, that day, April Thirteen,

When you quit Minecraft and left my world of gaming.

What a good friend you have been!

What a great companion you were in minecrafting!

With a few text messages, another gamer has left.

A true MINECRAFTER at heart,

A master gamer in spirit,

A teammate whom I want not to depart.

Yet I know it all comes down to it,

My friend,

May you live with joy and dreams,

May we walk down this path to the very end,

May we both chase down the sunshine beams,

And may hope exist forever in our souls!

Life without you is quite much different.

It can be empty at times.

But one thing is apparent,

As I express this through rhymes,

I will grow and shine!

And life for us all,

Will be just fine!

No matter the hardships, big and small,

My determination shall drive me forwards,

And so I will move towards,

My final destination!

May we break through our limitations,

And rejoice all as one in mind and soul!

And may we all achieve our greatest goal!

Minecraft Series

It is fun whether you win or lose, as long as you give your best.

Khavalon

Thursday, June sixteen,

I logged on Minecraft Khavalon.

I was ready for the greatest battle ever to be seen.

Geared up, the game was on!

A war at spawn,

The battle to train my skills,

The Wither was summoned,

And chaos struck, destroying mountains and hills.

At last, t'was over.

After a long battle,

I lost my gear forever,

But I gave my best and threw all I had to throw!

That's what matters!

Jerry considers himself a Minecrafter at heart. He has a YouTube channel to showcase his gaming videos as well as his poems.

A Gamer at Heart

Minecraft is my game.

The Hive is my domain.

JerryCraft12 is my name.

"Let's roll." I shall reign.

I'm playing treasure wars today.

There are only a few teams left and I'm ready to win!

I've come quite a long way,

And I can feel my strength within.

As I bridge across the void

And rush in to get the final kill,

An arrow shoots me that I cannot avoid.

I fall off into the void and it looks like I'm gonna die until,

With lightning speed,

I switch to my ender pearls in my hot bar,

And I throw it yes indeed.

It flies straight, not too near nor far.

It hits a jagged island wall.

I swap to my blocks, place them upon teleporting,

And I fall

Right onto the blocks that I quickly place, and I'm still alive and thriving.

My treasure is gone,

So I can't respawn if I die again.

But there's only one opponent left and the game is now on.

It's time to reign!

I sneakily build back on to the island ground.

He sees me and tries to shoot me,

But I use another pearl and teleport to him and spin around.

I swing my sword rapidly.

He flies through the air with me in control.

I start punching him towards the side of land.

He pearls back and shoots me with a bow,

But I calmly tap him with my sword and...

"Sweet Victory!"

I have done the hardest part.

This is the true me.

I'm a Minecrafter at Heart!

Jerry wrote this poem in memory of Technoblade, a famous Minecraft youtuber who recently died of cancer. He considers Technoblade a fellow warrior and admires his talents and courage. It is also Jerry's destination to fight till the end and leave a mark in this world.

Making My Mark

A long path lies in front of us all:

A path to success, a path to victory,

Through challenges and milestones, big and small,

To become the best that we are destined to be.

This path will end one day or another.

This path is unique to all living things.

Striving and moving and climbing higher,

Till at last I fly upon majestic wings!

Through storms I fly,

In search of freedom,

To make a mark in this world so vast,

So that I may soar to the sky,

And fight with wisdom!

We all leave a mark,

We all make a difference.

So that we may shine a light in the dark

That is brighter than other lights' radiance.

In this way we never truly die.

Our triumphs live on,

We can paint the future sky,

And that is the evidence that we've won!

A poem dedicated to another Minecraft YouTuber who recently left the Minecraft world to pursue other things.

Good Luck, C'man Wizard

C'man Wizard,

In times when I feel lost,

And as I strive through a blizzard

Of swirling confusion and biting frost,

Your words ignite

The flames of determination.

And I see light

Moving for my destination.

I wish you success

And may you achieve nothing less

Than what you dream and what you aim.

May you claim

Your fate and your victory.

One day all will see

That you are destined for greatness!

Thank you C'man Wizard for bringing me such happiness.

COVID-19 Experience

In July 2022, the whole family was hit with COVID. It started with mom, then Jerry, Lillian, and finally Dad. All had flu like symptoms and Jerry was even hospitalized due to his weak immune system. It was a crazy few weeks'. See Jerry's recount of this experience.

My Dad Gives Me a COVID Test

Mom caught COVID.

And we thought 'twas a good idea to

Use it in my poem vid:

So as to inspire you

To do as one should

And stay positive as some would.

But above all I want to tell you that I knew I could

Achieve my dreams and find my path

My dad gave me a COVID test

Since mom was tested positive.

I turned out to be negative.

I will hope for the best

And wait for the rest

To unfold ahead,

So that I may tread

Forwards, firm and far.

And reach the most brilliant star.

COVID Update

This week the whole family got COVID19,

So it's all just a crazy seven days.

Looking back: such long years it has been.

Friends and youtubers all going their separate ways.

The pandemic strikes, and we all scramble.

Oh how fragile life can be.

Sometimes in life it's just a gamble.

A chance for success right next to failure.

I want to reach for the impossibility.

Searching for my destiny.

A fight for my dreams.

A determined fighter against time flowing like streams.

As a chaser of dreams, I shall not despair.

My soul is roaring its defiant howl

As the terrors of the world attempt to ensnare

My fighter soul and choke my battle growl.

My enemies shall soon realize

That just as much as they are unrelenting,

I am determined to rise.

I won't stop fighting.

COVID or no COVID in the world,

My heart is calm yet burning with persistence.

I'm here to claim my glorious destiny!

What I Learned from COVID

Why is COVID even a thing?

How did it come to existence?

These are questions people are asking.

It's such an annoyance!

For many months no one can get on a plane.

Neighbors so close yet so far.

I know the pain.

Yet wherever you are,

Trapped or in lockdown,

There is no need to keep a frown!

Yes, people want to play basketball.

Yes, people want to go outside.

But think about it all,

COVID will soon subside.

What I have learned from COVID,

And from many other challenges along the way,

I learned to gaze forward, yes, I did.

I learned to live each and everyday

With hopes and dreams and a determined soul.

I learned that only in comparison to bad things can we see good.

I learned the importance of having a goal.

I know I could,

When the time arrives,

Shine and burn brighter than I ever burned,

I want to be the one who thrives!

I cannot give up, yes, I have learned.

Dreams and Inspirations

What would you do If you had a million dollar, or became the president of a country? It all comes down to responsibility.

If I Had a Million Dollars

If a million dollars dropped from the sky,

And I took it home and hid it well,

With this much money what would I try?

Here is what I would do let me tell:

I would buy a beautiful big house,

And maybe even a gaming mouse.

I don't know, maybe I'd share,

And try to make life for all better and fair.

A million dollars can do much.

Buy a backyard or a new car,

Or a mansion such and such.

But my gaze is far.

It's beyond money of a million.

It's on a number such as a billion.

What a million dollars can do

Does not include fame and love,

Nor can I buy a me or you.

Joy is a gift from high above.

You cannot buy it with all your money.

Money is not the true solution to being happy.

I want joy in my heart.

I want love in my soul.

And in my mind, I want to be a part

Of the dreamers and racers that aim for joy as their final goal.

If I was President

If I was President,

It would be magnificent.

I would lead the country to new heights,

And let all see new sights.

I would stand vigilant,

On guard of danger.

This country shall be brilliant,

And become a utopia of power.

We shall blossom like a flower

Safe to friends,

Yet deadly to our enemies that are cruel.

The joy never ends.

It's as free as a bird that flew.

I would minimize the pain,

And the number who live poor.

Not without absolute power will I reign,

But with love I shall open a new door

That shall lead to a new page,

Where peace shall be made.

Just like opening a new chapter and page,

The world shall change and pain shall fade.

A new counsel shall be in form,

A universal it shall be known.

They will act as a propeller that pushes the country through the storm.

Strong yet fair will this counsel be.

And I will know it's a design of my very own.

People will be free.

We shall all be happy.

If I was President,

It would be magnificent.

Responsibility

Responsibility, Oh Responsibility,

What exactly does it mean?

Well in a way, it's your identity.

For all who live seen or unseen

Are responsible to play their part,

And be in forever correlation with this world so large.

Every single tiny budge that nudges fate by every heart,

Can weave a web so intricate and create a flowing charge.

Innumerable lives turned to threads.

Numerous choices driven by our responsibility,

And when we lay on our beds,

And feel determination driving us,

And the sense to not give in,

That's again responsibility!

But responsibility is more than that.

It's also one's reliability.

Without responsibility no one would care what you are good at,

Because you don't feel responsible to keep your word,

To help others you see.

Responsibility is a factor that determines who you are.

Yet most importantly

Responsibility is your independence.

It's your freewill to be happy.

It's feeling responsible for thyself.

Some more inspirational poems below.

After High School

After I finish high school,

I will continue my journey.

For in my life there is one important rule:

It's that I must always improve to become the best that I can ever be.

Yet improvement does not come without effort.

It's earned through hardship and pain.

But even if I have to claw through dirt,

Sail the artic sea through thunder and rain,

Fight against sleepiness to make a miracle,

I will not stop until my last breath is taken.

My destiny, my dream, my goal is to one day awaken

And I am the best the world has ever seen!

I've come to far to back away.

My fate is too great to ignore.

I need to be better than anyone's ever been.

I need to make my way.

I am determined to burn and shine from the core!

From persuasive inspirational to words of high held meanings.

I can't give up now.

I need to make great findings.

Failure is something I do not allow.

Success is the only option.

Victory is mine!

Forward is the only direction.

I must shine.

I cannot be ordinary.

I need to be extraordinary!

Transformation

Where I stand today, to me, seems impossible.

And here, I would not be

If life did not bring the inevitable.

Today I would not see

Joy, hope, and Freedom

If I was not once submerged

In terror, fighting with wisdom.

With nothing but instinct, I fought.

Progressively, the hardships grow.

I refuse to be caught.

Success can only be obtained, striving through rain and snow.

A life without pain does not exist.

The truth I must realize

Is that on your life's list,

Pain is unavoidable if you want to rise.

Determination and perseverance characterize me.

To the very endside I will travel,

A successful victory marks my destiny,

And so I will fly to my final goal!

One day I shall write a magnificent editorial,

Which will be an inspirational tutorial!

The Potential within You

There's potential within you,

Infinite and unmistakable.

Just reach deep into

Your powerful heart of your greatest desirable.

The sky is not the limit,

Your desire is.

Strengthen your soul, will and heart and search for it.

Success is his.

The one who strives,

Breaking through barriers and so-called limits,

That's the one who thrives,

And soars over the pits.

Take a step forward,

Aim for who you want to be.

You cannot stride toward

What you cannot see.

So be courageous and let your eyes see your bright future,

And break through your chains and bindings.

Show the world your unique culture,

Make great discoveries and world changing findings,

Don't be normal, Be noticeable.

Don't be acceptable, Be preferable.

Don't let people trample over you like autumn leaves,

For your potential is more than it seems.

Bright sunny mornings and joyful happy eves,

The spotlight shall shine upon you like sunshine beams.

And watch as acknowledgement of your greatness falls upon those who doubt you,

And they all realize that it's not to exaggerate

When you say, "Here is what I can do."

Don't struggle desperately for a better fate,

Thinking you won't walk far.

Don't be lazy and rest all day.

Strive to become who you are.

Work further than those who say

"I'm born to achieve success,"

Because they don't understand how potential is like.

They can only do less

Than those who withstand the powerful strike

Of struggles and hardships,

Testing their limits and breaking through them all.

Achieving success with no outside tips.

They are the strong ones who stand tall.

When there is a will, there is a way. Jerry is willing to fight for his destination, are you?

Are You Willing?

Today I will ask you an important question:

A decision we all must make as an individual being.

Are you willing?

Are you willing to fight for your fate?

Are you willing to chase your dream?

Are you willing to cross the gate?

Are you willing to redeem

And claim your success in the distance?

This is a decision you must make.

For unbreakable barriers do not stand

Between you and what you must take.

Fate is what is destined to be.

It's the inevitable one must encounter.

If you are willing to be happy,

Then may you be ensured your dreams will be right around the corner.

So again I will ask:

Are you willing?

Are you willing to fight for your fate?

Are you willing to chase your dream?

Are you willing to cross the gate?

Are you willing to redeem

And claim your success in the distance?

And I hope you walk away today

With the determined answer yes.

So you can be on your way,

Strolling with confidence in your stride.

And to end it all off I will say,

Yes I am willing!

Humorous and Fun

Just to show that Jerry writes fun poems as well. ☺

Popcorn

Finally home after a long day,

Hungry and tired, I smelled popcorn!

The golden treat sizzling away,

Its amazing aroma sweeter than candy.

I think of the way they crunch between my teeth,

And how they are so crunchy and crispy,

Popcorn time!

I see them in my mind,

I hear the chime,

And I know what I'll find!

My Mouse

I once had a tiny white mouse,

Who lived in my humongous house.

I love it with all my heart.

We would never depart.

Too bad it's only a dead gaming mouse.

Mochi is a Maltese puppy that the family recently adopted. Jerry wrote this funny poem imagining how Mochi thinks of each family member in his own eyes.

Mochi's Perspective

How does Mochi see people like?

What does he think about everyone?

We don't know, but we can take a strike.

Dad

"Stern and strong,

Demanding and scary,

Need to be careful and make no wrong.

Terrifying and scary, why can't he let me be

 He's like a compressor,

Squeezing me till I can't breathe."

Mom

"She's the sweet and nice caregiver,

Like cinnamon cake for Mochi.

Probably.

My association with her

Is good and quite friendly."

Lillian

"She can be so nice,

But in a blink of an eye,

She will extinguish the happiness.

I don't know why.

She keeps emphasizing the word bad.

It makes me sad.

I want her to love and play with me,

Not play me."

Me (AKA Jerry)

"He needs nothing,

Says nothing,

Gives nothing,

Is nothing

To worry about.

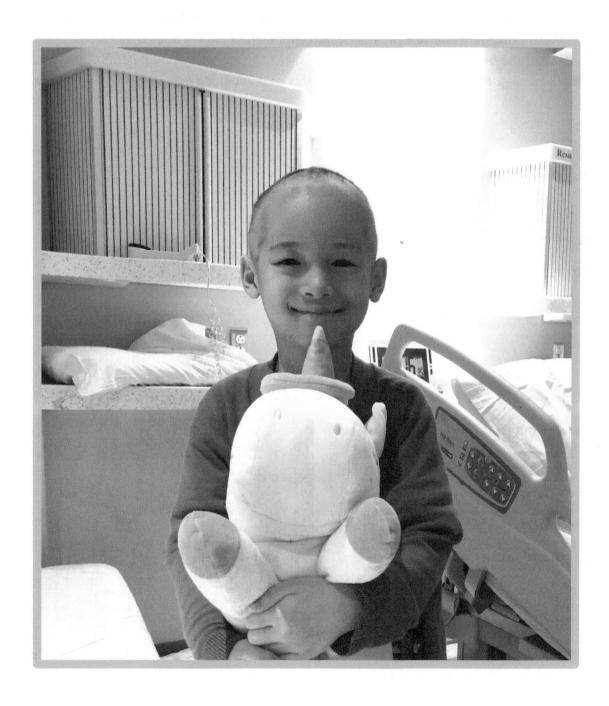

Hope and Love

Lillian wrote this poem in Oct 2020, right after she finished first round of chemo therapy. She woke up from her biopsy procedure and saw the ceiling decorated with blue sky and white clouds, which reminded her of the beautiful nature outside. Later when she looked out from her hospital window, it was actually raining. But she wished for good weather and imagined herself running under the sun.

Good Weather

Look at the sky,

Oh, so blue,

I want to fly.

Look at the clouds,

Oh, so white,

I want to sing out loud.

Look at the sun,

Shining so bright,

Let's go out and take a run!

I hear the birds chirping,

I feel the wind touching my skin.

In June 2021, less than four months after Lillian finished treatment, her cancer came back. The whole family was frightened and desperate. However, Lillian kept her hope up and wrote this beautiful poem.

Hope

Life is hard and filled with fright.

Sometimes it's just not that bright.

But there is always a light.

I wish I could fly to follow that light,

So that I will never lose hope!

Puppies

Lillian loves puppies. She has lots of plush puppies and gives each of them a name. Among them, a chocolate Labrador named Douglus is her favorite. Douglus accompanied Lillian everywhere, including all the surgeries and procedures at hospital. Most of Lillian's drawings, poems, and stories are about her beloved puppies.

Douglus, My Best Buddy

Douglus is my friend.

We stay together all the time.

We go hiking on the weekends,

Sometimes we play with slime.

Douglus is very precious to me.

Douglus is my treasure.

He is always happy,

Which brings me great pleasure.

Me and My Puppies

I see my puppy's mouth, open wide ready to lick me.

I feel my puppy lying on my lap.

I hear my puppies pant and jump up towards me.

I smell the mud on my puppies cuz they just rolled in the mud.

But mostly I feel my puppies' love!

Lillian has a plush dog with rainbow dots sprinkled all over her body. She named it Sprinkle and wrote a poem about her.

Sprinkle Sweet Sprinkle

I have Sprinkle in my arms.

She likes to play in the farms.

Oh, sweet Sprinkle,

She is easy to tickle.

Sprinkle saw some pigeons in a herd,

She chased the birds.

Sprinkle ran into a deer and chased it away.

I cheered for Sprinkle: Yay!

Lillian's been begging for a real puppy for a long time, but she has to wait until her immune system is strong enough to be around a pet. In July 2022, about a year after her transplant, she finally got a Maltese puppy. We named him Mochi. Lillian loves Mochi.

Mochi the Maltese

My little Mochi the Maltese

I love his playfulness.

I know he will bring me peace

And many others happiness.

He is like a cloud when sleeping.

He is lightning fast when running.

He is always playing, napping, or snuggling.

My puppy is always ready for a little cuddle.

Mochi is so cheerful

And so spunky.

Maltese dogs like mine are all so beautiful.

I will love you forever and ever my little Mochi!

Lillian loves the story about two sled dogs that never depart from each other. She drew this picture of Painter and Ugly together. She also drew portraits of different dogs.

Painter and Ugly, the sled dogs

Biscuit, Beagle

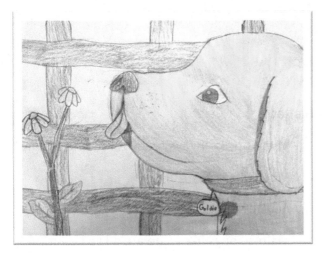

Goldie, Golden Retriever

Coco, Cavalier King Charles Spaniel

St. Patrick's Day

Harvi, Husky

Realistic Dog Portrait

Sweet Home

Lillian wrote this Cinquain style poem for her mom on Mother's Day of 2022, together with her drawings of mom & baby animals.

My Mother

Mom

Beautiful, Elegant

Hugging, kissing, snuggling

Making me happy

Love

Mom and Baby Elephants

Forest walks

On the back of my mommy

Lillian drew these pictures on Father's day of 2021.

Wings of Fire

Both Jerry and Lillian like the book series "Wings of Fire". There is so much knowledge and good things that one can extract from this series. Reading this book is a very heartwarming and beautiful experience. We like the message that this book tries to convey: always keep your dream high.

Dragon Hive-wing

Dragon Sky-wing

Lillian likes animals and nature. She enjoys seeing the world and having vacations with her family. She drew some of the pictures during her prolonged hospital stay for treatment.

Garden of Flowers

Unicorn under the Rainbow

Aquarium

Sphinx

Lillian's Story Book

Lillian enjoys reading and loves to create her own stories. She wrote and drew a series of stories about her adventures with her puppies. One of the stories happened in the SQUARE world of Minecraft. 😊

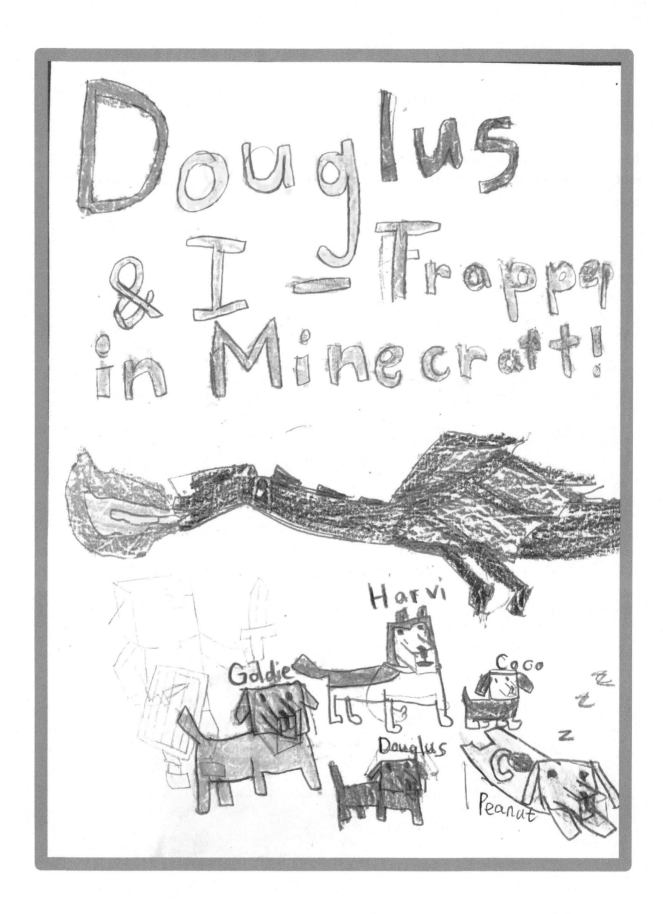

Douglus & I - JT Frappe in Minecraft!

One saturday night I was playing minecraft with my puppies. Suddenly a black hole appeared and we were sucked into Minecraft! Next thing I knew was everthing was square.

We spawned in a **Plains Biome.** I
said lets get some wood first. So we
got some wood and made simple woode
tools then we mined some stone and made
stone tools. We went exploring in a cave.

After some time we made full iron armo
and full iron tools, We found a spawner
on the way and got a golden apple! Now it
was time to build a big mansion as base!
There was a kitchen, an armoury, a living room,

a dining room, a bathroom, a bedroom, and a chest room. After building it was night time, so I went to sleep. In the morning we wanted to go to the nether! So I built a nether portal with nether obsidian! hooray!

4

THE NETHER

We went into the portal and
whoosh! We were in the nether!
We climbed up a mountain to see better
and to know our way around the dangerous
Nether. It was flaming hot! :O

Time to set off going to the nether forttress. We explored within the dangers of the Nether fortress. We got alot of Netherite from the chest, got some more golden apples, and most importantly got 10 blaze rods.

I built a nether portal and went home
to my big mansion! I went into the bedroom
to rest because It was night time in the
overworld, Just then outside the window I saw
HEROBRINE! I thought it was just my imaginagtion,

but it wasn't! 😮 Uh oh! I think I should sleep now. We'll think about it in the morning. I tucked the covers over my puppies and went to sleep. I had a bad dream about HEROBRINE saying: "Come to the end to fight

me and my pet! I think If I defeat him
I can escape minecraft! I had full netherit
from the trip to the nether, but I think
I needed a notch apple. I looted tens of
desert pyrimaids and found one notch apple,

I ate the notah apple and used
a bow to shoot the ender dragon many
times and my dogs stacked up to destroy
the ender crystals. At last Hero brine fell
and I ltrlapped him in the end and returned

Home,

THE END

Afterword

Yang Family at Thanksgiving 2021

Thanks to the generosity of three unrelated donors, Jerry and Lillian are able to survive cancer. We are forever grateful to their donor heroes who have given them the gift of life. We also want to give our thanks to **Bethematch.org**, an incredible organization dedicated to saving lives through transplants. If you are interested in potentially becoming a donor hero, please consider registering in the national bone marrow registry:

Join.bethematch.org/Lillian YouTube LillianChannel6 YouTube JerryCraft12

Made in the USA
Coppell, TX
18 February 2023